QUICK MENTAL MATHS

MENTAL RECALL PRACTICE FOR 9 YEAR OLDS

SCHOLASTIC MATHS SKILLS

D0315383

AUTHOR
William Hartley

DESIGNER
Mark Udall

EDITOR
Kate Pearce

ILLUSTRATIONS
Phil Garner

ASSISTANT EDITOR
Claire Miller

COVER ARTWORK
James Alexander/
David Oliver
(Berkeley
Studios)

SERIES DESIGNER
Anna Oliwa

Text © 1999 William Hartley
© 1999 Scholastic Ltd

Designed using Adobe Pagemaker
Published by Scholastic Ltd, Villiers House, Clarendon
Avenue, Leamington Spa, Warwickshire CV32 5PR

1234567890   9012345678

British Library Cataloguing-in-Publication Data
A catalogue record for this book is available from the
British Library.

ISBN 0-590-53921-3

SEC	SHEET	SHEET HEADING	SUGGESTED ORAL MATHS INPUT
COUNTING AND ORDERING	A1	COUNTING IN STEPS	Count on/back in steps less than 10 and in 10s and 100s.
	A2	PLACE VALUE	Practice digit values of four-digit numbers. See B/C11.
	A3	ORDERING WHOLE NUMBERS, FRACTIONS, DEC.	Order numbers to 10 000. Order small frac/dec amounts.
	A4	ESTIMATING AND APPROXIMATING	Use vocabulary such as roughly, nearly, about, etc.
	A5	ROUNDING WHOLE NUMBERS AND DECIMALS	Rounding two/three-digit numbers to the nearest 10/100.
	A6	TEST YOUR SKILLS 1 (A1–A3 REVIEW SHEET)	As for A1–A3.
	A7	TEST YOUR SKILLS 2 (A4–A5 REVIEW SHEET)	As for A4 and A5.
ADDITION AND SUBTRACTION	B1	ADDITION FACTS	Number bonds for multiples of 10, 20 and 30.
	B2	SUBTRACTION FACTS	Problems like: 40 – 15, 50 – 25, 45 – 15, 27 – 17, etc.
	B3	RELATIONSHIP BETWEEN + AND –	eg, 26 + 35, 35 + 26, 61 – 26, 61 – 35 (with bridging).
	B4	PAIRS AND DOUBLES	Number pairs to 50 (no bridging) and doubles to 20.
	B5	ADDING ORDER	Add TU/HTU (no bridging). Put the larger number first.
	B6	IDENTIFYING NEAR DOUBLES	eg, 70 + 60 = double 70 - 10 or double 60 + 10.
	B7	CALCULATION PATTERNS (+ AND –)	eg, 47 + 8 = 55, 47 + 18 = 65, 47 + 28 = 75, etc.
	B8	PARTITIONING AND RECOMBINING	Partition into 10s and 1s and add the 10s first.
	B9	BRIDGING AND ADJUSTING	Problems like: 37 + 8 = 37 + 3 + 5 = 45, etc.
	B10	+ AND – WHOLE NUMBERS, FRACTIONS, DECIMALS	U/TU to/from HTU with simple bridging.
	B11	PLACE VALUE WHEN ADDING AND SUBTRACTING	Decimal places in relation to money. See A2 and C11.
	B12	ADDING AND SUBTRACTING SEVERAL NUMBERS	Adding/subtracting 3/4 numbers and crossing the tens.
	B13	TEST YOUR SKILLS 1 (B1–B6 REVIEW SHEET)	As for B1–B6.
	B14	TEST YOUR SKILLS 2 (B7–B12 REVIEW SHEET)	As for B7–B12.
MULTIPLICATION AND DIVISION	C1	MULTIPLICATION FACTS	Multiplication facts for the 2 to 6, 8 and 10 times tables.
	C2	DIVISION FACTS	Division facts for the 2 to 6, 8 and 10 times tables.
	C3	RELATIONSHIP BETWEEN × AND ÷	Practice breaking numbers into sub-sets (× and ÷).
	C4	DOUBLES, HALVES, QUARTERS AND EIGHTHS	Practice ways to find doubles, halves, quarters, eighths.
	C5	PARTITIONING WHEN MULTIPLYING	Multiplying 10s first when multiplying TU by U.
	C6	DIVISION WITH REMAINDERS	Reinforce the meaning of 'left over' and 'remainder'.
	C7	CALCULATION PATTERNS (× AND ÷)	× and ÷ patterns in the 2 to 6 and 8 and 10 times tables.
	C8	FACTORS AND MULTIPLYING BY 10, 100, 1000	Factor games and decimal place shifting activities.
	C9	DIVIDING BY 10, 100, 1000	Division questions that involve decimal place shifting.
	C10	USING RELATED × AND ÷ FACTS	eg, Give four facts for the numbers 6, 5 and 30, and so on.
	C11	PLACE VALUE WHEN MULTIPLYING AND DIVIDING	ThHTU problems. ×/÷ to 2 dec place. See A2/B11.
	C12	× AND ÷ WHOLE NUMBERS, FRACTIONS, DECIMALS	Practice ×/÷ facts for tables 2–6. ×/÷ simple frac/dec.
	C13	TEST YOUR SKILLS 1 (C1–C6 REVIEW SHEET)	As for C1–C6.
	C14	TEST YOUR SKILLS 2 (C7–C12 REVIEW SHEET)	As for C7–C12.
MULTISTEP AND MIXED OPERATIONS	D1	ADDING, SUBTRACTING AND MULTIPLYING	Choose any adding, subtracting or multiplying activities.
	D2	MULTIPLYING, DIVIDING AND ADDING	Choose any multiplying, dividing or adding activities.
	D3	ADDING, MULTIPLYING AND SUBTRACTING	Choose any adding, multiplying or subtracting activities.
	D4	SUBTRACTING, DIVIDING AND ADDING	Choose any subtracting, dividing or adding activities.

ABOUT THE SERIES

Quick Mental Maths aims to help children develop quick mental recall strategies – both the instant recall of known facts and speedy methods of figuring out 'unknowns'. Number facts are the vital building blocks for calculation, and their easy access is the key to efficient, accurate and confident mental mathematical ability.

Quick Mental Maths is a series of six photocopiable books providing a mixture of problem-posing styles of mental number practice for children aged 6 to 11. The level of ability at which each book is pitched has been broadly determined from the recommendations of the National Numeracy *Framework* document. *Quick Mental Maths* can be used as an independent resource in its own right to support any of the UK curriculum documentation, but can also be used in conjunction with the other Scholastic series *Developing Mental Maths* and *Practising Mental Maths*.

The books will provide valuable reinforcement of number bonds and times tables and help to improve the children's mental agility, as well as consolidating and extending their knowledge and use of mathematical vocabulary. These worksheets could be used as regular number practice – perhaps with a short time allowed each day for the children to complete one or more sections of a worksheet – as pre-SATs reinforcement/assessment tasks, or as worthwhile homework pages. All photocopiable sheets are indicated by the icon ⓟ.

ABOUT THE BOOK STRUCTURE
IN-BUILT DIFFERENTIATION

Each of the six books in this series addresses the same mental maths content under the same worksheet heading in each book, but at an increasing level of complexity. Thus, for example, you will find that worksheet A2 is always 'Place value' and worksheet C6 is always about 'Division with remainders'. Therefore, differentiation in a mixed-ability class is made easy by using the same worksheet number from more than one book to provide the same material at different levels.

YOUR INPUT

In order to reinforce the intended strategy to be used by the children to complete each sheet, it is recommended that you engage in some oral maths work with the class before they start. A varied use of mathematical vocabulary is very important when doing this. Some brief guidance for this aspect of your lesson preparation is given alongside each worksheet heading on the 'Teacher's information chart' on the opposite page. (You will find other suitable oral maths activities described in detail in the Scholastic teachers' book *Developing Mental Maths with 7–9 year olds*.)

RECORD-KEEPING

The photocopiable record sheet on the next page is to facilitate your record-keeping and assessment. This can either be given to the child as a record of his or her achievement or used as a teacher's record of which pages have been completed by which children and with what degree of success.

CONTENT ORGANIZATION

Each book is split into four sections:
A Counting and ordering
B Addition and subtraction
C Multiplication and division
D Multistep and mixed operations
The activities on each worksheet in sections A–C concentrate on one strategy, offering instant recall practice, number and word problems and a more investigational extension activity. The intention is that the page represents an 'achievable minimum' for children working at that level and that the extension activity (indicated by the icon 📖) will only be attempted by the more able child using a separate maths book or blank paper which can then be included in his or her personal maths file. In this way, it is hoped that the less able child will be able to tackle the majority of the page, while the more able child also has a 'special challenge'.

At the end of each of the first three sections (A–C) you will find two review tests relating specifically to the content of the sheets in that section. The problems are numbered to key in with the worksheet pages to which the questions relate. These review sheets will provide you with an opportunity to assess how well each child is progressing with the strategies on the worksheets in that section.

The final section of worksheets (D) gives the children the chance to practise some of their developing skills using more involved mental operation sequences that often require them to hold on to an interim number. The sheets in this section will really challenge the children.

ANSWERS

The final pages of the book provide the answers to all, but the most open-ended, of the questions on each worksheet. Answers in bold indicate those numbers which are given on the worksheets.

ABOUT THIS BOOK

Quick Mental Maths for 9 year olds is intended for Year 4/P5 children working at NC/NIC Level 3 (NNP Year 4) or confidently within Scottish Level C. It is hoped the activities in this book will help to further extend the children's knowledge and understanding of place value, counting and times tables, and that it will lead children into adopting some of the many different strategies and techniques available to them for tackling daily mathematical situations with confidence and efficiency.

RECORD SHEET

SHEET NO	MARK	COMMENT
A1		
A2		
A3		
A4		
A5		
A6		
A7		
B1		
B2		
B3		
B4		
B5		
B6		
B7		
B8		
B9		
B10		
B11		
B12		
B13		
B14		

SHEET NO	MARK	COMMENT
C1		
C2		
C3		
C4		
C5		
C6		
C7		
C8		
C9		
C10		
C11		
C12		
C13		
C14		
D1		
D2		
D3		
D4		

COUNTING IN STEPS (INC NEGATIVE NUMBERS)

1. Fill in the missing numbers in these series.

a.

£3.25	£3.31			£3.49		

b.

	475m	450m			375m	

2a. Count back in 5s from 100 to 50.

100 _____ 50

b. If you continued counting back in 5s would 35 be in your sequence? ☐

c. Fill in the missing numbers on this number line.

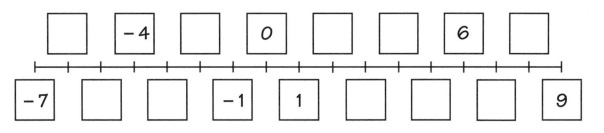

☐	−4	☐	0	☐	☐	6	☐

−7	☐	☐	−1	1	☐	☐	☐	9

3a. Complete these sequences for the ×2, ×4, ×3 and ×6 tables.

20			26						38	
40		48				64				
30				42						60
60	66							108		

b. What do you notice about the numbers you have just written in the table sequences above?

Starting at 100, count ten steps forward in the following amounts: 3, 6 and 8. Starting at 200, count ten steps backward in the following amounts: 2, 4 and 5.

QUICK MENTAL MATHS

PLACE VALUE

COUNTING AND ORDERING

1. Write these amounts in figures.

a. twenty-nine _____

b. three hundred and six _____

c. six hundred and thirty _____

d. two thousand and four _____

e. three hundred and twenty _____

f. eight thousand and sixty _____

g. nine thousand, four hundred and seventy _____

h. five thousand, six hundred and fifty-two _____

i. seven thousand, nine hundred and ten _____

2. Write these amounts in words.

a. 72 _____

b. 608 _____

c. 820 _____

d. 35 _____

e. 4250 _____
_____

f. 2405 _____
_____

3. Write the correct numbers in the spaces.

a. $1234 = 1000 + 200 + 30 + $ _____

b. _____ $= 8000 + 700 + 60 + 5$

c. $2659 = $ _____ $+ 600 + 50 + 9$

d. $6000 + 700 + $ _____ $+ 1 = 6721$

e. $9583 = 9000 + $ _____ $+ 80 + 3$

f. $3724 = 700 + 4 + 20 + $ _____

Draw seven columns with these headings:

−1000	−100	−10	Number	+10	+100	+1000

Write these numbers in the centre column: 3040, 5395, 7002, 1256, 4609, 6048, 8794 and 7593. Now add 10, 100 and 1000 and subtract 10, 100 and 1000 from each number.

ORDERING WHOLE NUMBERS, FRACTIONS, DECIMALS

1. Fill in the boxes with the correct sign, < or >, so that these number sentences make sense. The first one has been done for you.

a.	1654	>	1546	e.	$\frac{1}{2}$		$\frac{1}{3}$	i.	0.25		0.36
b.	201		210	f.	$\frac{1}{7}$		$\frac{1}{9}$	j.	1.30		1.04
c.	−10		−12	g.	$\frac{1}{10}$		$\frac{1}{4}$	k.	0.05		0.50
d.	9242		9422	h.	$\frac{1}{5}$		$\frac{1}{8}$	l.	3.72		2.27

2. Answer the following questions by writing 'Yes' or 'No' below.

a. Is 1265 as many as 1562? _____

b. Is 29 + 21 equal to 76 − 26? _____

c. Is 3003 fewer than 3030? _____

d. Is 7025 more than 7250? _____

e. Is 5252 smaller than 5225? _____

f. Is 6074 larger than 6047? _____

Write down the answers to these problems.

g. Which is heavier: 3725kg or 3527kg? _____

h. Which is lighter: 8020g or 8002g? _____

i. Write a number more than 6999. _____

3. Arrange these numbers in order of size, starting with the largest.

a. 6789   7896   8967   6978   6987   9876   7898

_____

b. £1.50   £6.50   £5.60   £5.10   £6.80   £5.80   £8.60   £6.08

_____

Write down the names of the children in your group or class. Then sort the names according to how many letters there are in each one.

ESTIMATING AND APPROXIMATING

1. From the list, pick the amount that you think will be nearest to the actual answer of the problem and write it in the first box. Then write the correct answer in the second box.

12   650   200   3000   20   400   80   500   30   2000

a. 32cm – 14cm [ ] [ ]   **f.** 89m + 407m [ ] [ ]

b. 659ml + 21ml [ ] [ ]   **g.** 300mm × 7 [ ] [ ]

c. 5 × 15hrs [ ] [ ]   **h.** £78 ÷ 6 [ ] [ ]

d. 140km ÷ 5 [ ] [ ]   **i.** 460m – 63m [ ] [ ]

e. £247 – £35 [ ] [ ]   **j.** 239g + 3001g [ ] [ ]

2. Estimate the numbers marked by the arrows on the number line.

0   1000

3a. Write a number that is roughly a quarter of:

300 _____   165 _____   2450 _____   5980 _____   7999 _____

b. Write a number that is roughly a half of:

199 _____   151 _____   2999 _____   1202 _____   1445 _____

Guess the distance on a map from one place to another. Write down your answer. Use the scale on the map to help you find out how close your answer was. Try again!

COUNTING AND ORDERING

ROUNDING WHOLE NUMBERS AND DECIMALS

1a. Round these distances to the nearest 10 kilometres.

113km _____   291km _____   655km _____   4009km _____

b. Round these prices to the nearest pound.

£8.53 _____   £10.24 _____   £9.99 _____   £0.65 _____

c. Round these lengths to the nearest metre.

720cm _____   350cm _____   1045cm _____   2664cm _____

2a. Round these distances from London to the nearest 10 miles and then to the nearest 100 miles.

b. Carry out these instructions.

York	209 miles		
Norwich	115 miles		
Leeds	196 miles		
Cardiff	155 miles		
Brighton	53 miles		
Glasgow	405 miles		

Write a number that is half-way between 3000 and 6000.

_____

Write a number between 100 and 200 that is nearer to 200 than 100.

_____

3. Round these amounts to the nearest whole one.

a. 3.6 hours _____

b. 10.3 litres _____

c. 5.8 metres _____

d. 122.4km _____

e. 25.5cm _____

f. £1.75 _____

g. 2.3 hours _____

h. 7.7 litres _____

Make up different four-digit numbers using the following sets of digits and write each number to the nearest 100: (1,2,3,4) (5,6,7,8) (9,1,2,3) (4,5,6,7).

NAME _____ CLASS _____

TEST YOUR SKILLS 1 (A1–A3)

COUNTING AND ORDERING

A1 Fill in the missing amounts in these series.

a.	£2.28			£2.07	£2.00	

b.	345g	395g				595g

c.		5725	5425		4825	

d. Count back in 4s from 95 to 55.

95 _____ 55

e. If you went below 55 would 35 be in your sequence?

_____

A2 Read and answer these questions carefully.

a. Make the largest number you can from the digits given.

5,6,5,2 _____   9,9,8,8 _____   3,0,6,0 _____

b. How many units in two thousand and forty-nine? _____

c. What does the digit 7 stand for in 3726? _____

d. Write down the number that is the same as five thousand,

four hundred and eight. _____

A3

a. Arrange these numbers in order of size starting with the largest.

b. Arrange these amounts in order of size starting with the smallest.

7439	3140	3041	7394
7934	3104	7943	8506

$\frac{1}{2}$ 0.3   0.7 $\frac{2}{5}$ 1

0.1 $\frac{9}{10}$ $\frac{4}{5}$ 0.6 $\frac{1}{5}$

_____   _____

_____   _____

P

QUICK MENTAL MATHS

TOTAL

TEST YOUR SKILLS 2 (A4–A5)

A4 Estimate the numbers marked by the arrows on the number
a. line.

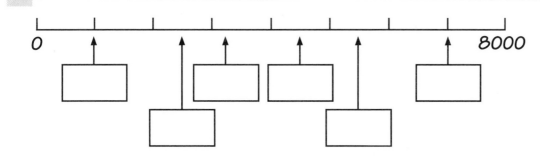

b. Shade in the best approximation for the problem shown at the
top of each column.

302 + 599	706 – 102	99 × 7	57 ÷ 3
300 + 500	600 – 110	630	171
300 + 99	700 – 100	900	20
300 + 600	700 – 200	700	573

A5 Round the lengths of these rivers to the nearest 10, 100 and
a. 1000kms.

Name	Length (km)	Nearest 10km	Nearest 100km	Nearest 1000km
Amazon	6516			
Zaire	4373			
Lena	4256			
Nile	6669			

Round these amounts to the nearest whole one.

b. 2.1 hours _____

c. 4.8 litres _____

d. 3.4 metres _____

e. 17.3cm _____

f. £3.51 _____

g. 2.7 hours _____

TOTAL

COUNTING AND ORDERING

ADDITION FACTS

1. Write in the missing measures.

a. 33 min + 17 min = _____

b. 28mm + _____ = 50mm

c. _____ + 85kg = 100kg

d. 76m + 24m = _____

e. _____ + 7 litres = 8000ml

f. 620g + _____ = 1kg

g. _____ + £37.00 = £90.00

h. 270km + 330km = _____

i. _____ +61p = 80p

j. 14 hours + _____ = 40 hours

2. Find the total of each of these pairs of numbers.

a. 42, 18 [ ]

b. 36, 34 [ ]

c. 27, 63 [ ]

d. 54, 26 [ ]

e. 27, 53 [ ]

f. 18, 72 [ ]

g. 43, 27 [ ]

h. 35, 45 [ ]

i. 6, 54 [ ]

j. 52, 18 [ ]

k. 33, 27 [ ]

l. 45, 45 [ ]

m. 72, 8 [ ]

n. 54, 16 [ ]

o. 61, 19 [ ]

3. Solve the problems below. Write your answers in words.

a. Find the sum of thirty-eight, twelve and forty. _____

b. What number is twenty-seven more than twenty-three? _____

c. How many would you have if you added 16, 20 and 34? _____

d. Increase eleven by nineteen and treble the answer. _____

e. Add the odd numbers between twelve and eighteen. _____

Look at your answers to part 2 and write down some different pairs of two-digit numbers that also add up to either 60, 70, 80 or 90.

QUICK MENTAL MATHS

SUBTRACTION FACTS

1. In the three columns below connect each subtraction to the correct answer.

a.			b.			c.		
50 – 45	15		30 – 15	5		20 – 15	10
30 – 5	10		40 – 5	40		40 – 10	5
40 – 25	5		50 – 10	20		50 – 20	45
20 – 10	25		40 – 35	15		50 – 30	30
50 – 25	10		30 – 25	5		40 – 30	30
30 – 20	25		40 – 20	35		50 – 5	20

2. Work out the answers to these number problems. Write your answers in words.

a. Find the difference between forty-seven and nineteen. _____

b. Decrease thirty-six by twenty-seven minus three. _____

c. Five hundred subtract 325. _____

d. What number is left when 56 is taken away from 98? _____

3. Fill in this chart.

–	47	40	37	49	45	60	39	50	46	35	48	36	38
23		17											
14						46							
34									12				
12													26
31				18									

 Ask your teacher for some squared paper. Draw a chart like the one above, but write some two-digit numbers larger than 50 across the top and the numbers 14 to 18 down the side. Fill it in.

QUICK MENTAL MATHS

RELATIONSHIP BETWEEN + AND −

ADDITION AND SUBTRACTION

1. Fill in the missing bits to complete these sets. The first one has been done for you.

a. 46 + 39 = 85,   39 + 46 = 85,   85 − 46 = 39,   85 − 39 = 46

b. 54 + 27= _____ ,   81 − 27= _____ ,   81 − 54 = 27,   _____

c. 29 + 48 = _____ ,   48 + 29 = 77,   _____ , 77 − 48 = _____

d. 57 + 36 = 93,   _____ , 93 − 36 = _____ , 36 + 57 = _____

e. _____ , 89 − 74 = _____ , 74 + 15 = _____ , 15 + 74 = _____

2. The four sentences below all have the amounts £35.00, £72.00 and £37.00 in them. In the same way write out four sentences using the amounts £81.00, £38.00 and £43.00.

£37.00 add £35.00 equals £72.00   _____

35.00 plus £37.00 equals £72.00   _____

£72.00 minus £37.00 equals £35.00   _____

£72.00 subtract £35.00 equals £37.00 _____

3a. In the right-hand box, write an addition fact using all three numbers in the left-hand box.

b. In the right-hand box, write a subtraction fact using all three numbers from the left-hand box.

23, 28, 51	23 + 28 = 51		39, 24, 63	63 − 24 = 39
35, 71, 36			57, 26, 83	
72, 45, 27			91, 28, 63	
56, 90, 34			37, 44, 81	
25, 46, 71			28, 63, 35	

Using the numbers 41, 65, 106, 24 and 17, make up some three-figure addition and subtraction facts, for example, 106 − 41 = 65.

QUICK MENTAL MATHS

PAIRS AND DOUBLES

1. Write in the answers to these addition doubles.

a. 5 + 5 = ☐   **e.** 10 + 10 = ☐   **i.** 12 + 12 = ☐   **m.** 17 + 17 = ☐

b. 7 + 7 = ☐   **f.** 8 + 8 = ☐   **j.** 15 + 15 = ☐   **n.** 19 + 19 = ☐

c. 9 + 9 = ☐   **g.** 13 + 13 = ☐   **k.** 16 + 16 = ☐   **o.** 18 + 18 = ☐

d. 6 + 6 = ☐   **h.** 11 + 11 = ☐   **l.** 14 + 14 = ☐   **p.** 20 + 20 = ☐

2. Write down the difference between each of these amounts and 100.

a. 53 centimetres _____   **g.** 47 centimetres _____

b. 42 millilitres _____   **h.** sixteen grams _____

c. nineteen hours _____   **i.** twenty-one litres _____

d. eighty-five pence _____   **j.** thirty-eight metres _____

e. 67 kilometres _____   **k.** 70 kilograms _____

f. ninety-four pounds _____   **l.** 58 minutes _____

3. Fill in the missing numbers in these subtraction halves.

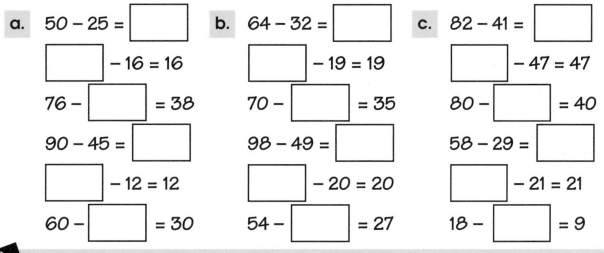

a. 50 − 25 = ☐   **b.** 64 − 32 = ☐   **c.** 82 − 41 = ☐

☐ − 16 = 16   ☐ − 19 = 19   ☐ − 47 = 47

76 − ☐ = 38   70 − ☐ = 35   80 − ☐ = 40

90 − 45 = ☐   98 − 49 = ☐   58 − 29 = ☐

☐ − 12 = 12   ☐ − 20 = 20   ☐ − 21 = 21

60 − ☐ = 30   54 − ☐ = 27   18 − ☐ = 9

Make a list of the numbers from 21 to 50. Next to each number write down its double. Carry on past 50 if you have time.

ADDING ORDER

1. Rearrange these sums so that you start with the largest number and end with the smallest. The first one has been done for you.

a.	37	+	4	+	151	=	151	+	37	+	4	=	192
b.	235	+	9	+	12	=		+		+		=	
c.	55	+	320	+	8	=		+		+		=	
d.	24	+	11	+	465	=		+		+		=	
e.	16	+	756	+	14	=		+		+		=	

2. Answer these questions. Remember the rule about putting the largest number first.

a. Liam spent 20p and had 59p left.

How much did he have to begin with? _____

b. Increase fifteen by forty-seven. _____

c. In a money box there are seven FIVES, six TENS and four ONES.

What is the total value of all the coins? _____

3. Make up ten add sums using all these numbers. Use each number only once. Add TU to HTU. Write the largest number first. Now work out your sums.

185	18	155	59
91	145	175	88
26	115	42	125
165	54	105	73
37	135	65	195

_____ + _____ = _____   _____ + _____ = _____

_____ + _____ = _____   _____ + _____ = _____

_____ + _____ = _____   _____ + _____ = _____

_____ + _____ = _____   _____ + _____ = _____

_____ + _____ = _____   _____ + _____ = _____

Make up your own addition sums using three two-digit numbers.
Put the largest number first and work out the answers in your head.

P

QUICK MENTAL MATHS

IDENTIFYING NEAR DOUBLES

B6

1. Add these near doubles. Look at the examples first which are there to help you.

30 + 28 = 58. This sum can be done quickly by saying double 30 minus 2.

47 + 45 = 92. This sum can be done quickly by saying double 45 plus 2.

a. 60 + 62 = ☐   **e.** 70 + 73 = ☐   **i.** 120 + 117 = ☐

b. 50 + 53 = ☐   **f.** 40 + 42 = ☐   **j.** 90 + 89 = ☐

c. 30 + 31 = ☐   **g.** 130 + 131 = ☐   **k.** 110 + 108 = ☐

d. 80 + 84 = ☐   **h.** 140 + 145 = ☐   **l.** 150 + 148 = ☐

2. Here are two other ways to *think* when adding near doubles.

$$76 + 78 = 80 + 80 - 4 - 2 = 154$$

$$80 + 90 = 80 + 80 + 10 \text{ or } 90 + 90 - 10$$

Write out the *thinking* process when you do these sums.

a. £47 + £48 = _____   **c.** 70m + 80m = _____

b. 88p + 86p = _____   **d.** 70g + 60g = _____

3. Look for doubles to help you answer these problems.

a. Find the total of forty-six and forty-eight. _____

b. Add one hundred and forty and one hundred and fifty. _____

c. What number is fifty-eight more than fifty-six? _____

 Add some three-digit numbers that are near doubles and write out your thinking in full. Like this: 320 + 316 = (320 + 320) – 4 = 636.

B7

CALCULATION PATTERNS (+ AND –)

ADDITION AND SUBTRACTION

1. Fill in the missing numbers in these calculation patterns.

a. | 7 | +4 | | +6 | | +40 | | +60 | | +400 | |

b. | 418 | –300 | | –70 | | –30 | | –7 | | –3 | |

c. | 6 | +2 | | +8 | | +20 | | +80 | | +200 | |

d. | 622 | –500 | | –50 | | –50 | | –5 | | –5 | |

2. Look at these addition squares and then fill them in. The first one has been done for you.

12	12	24
15	13	28
27	25	52

	14	25
9		21
	26	

16	8	
	15	32
33		

20		70
	35	
45	85	

3. Study these subtraction grids carefully and then complete them.

–	41	42	43	44
26				18
27			16	
28		14		
29	12			

–	90
25	
35	
45	
55	

–	156	157	158	159
12				
23				
34				
45				

Ask your teacher for some squared paper. Draw ten small subtraction grids like the middle one above. Write the same numbers down the side but this time subtract them from any three-digit multiples of ten.

QUICK MENTAL MATHS

PARTITIONING AND RECOMBINING

1. The sum below shows the *thinking stages* you might use to get the right answer.

$$48 + 65 = (48 + 2) + (65 - 2) = 50 + 63 = 113$$

Do this sum and write out all your *thinking stages* in the same way as the example above.

a. 27 + 68 = _____

Look at this example. Now do the first sum below in the same way and try to *think* like that for the others

$$237 + 8 = 237 + 3 + 5 = 240 + 5 = 245$$

b. 438 + 9 = _____

c. 6 + 947 = _____   768 + 8 = _____   526 + 6 = _____   7 + 699 = _____

2. Do the first sum in the same way as the example below, then try to *think* like that for the others.

$$33 + 48 = (30 + 40) + (3 + 8) = 70 + 11 = 81$$

a. 52 + 26 = _____

b. 41 + 37 = _____   79 + 18 = _____   85 + 64 = _____   94 + 57 = _____

Look at the *thinking stages* for this subtraction. Try to work out the other subtractions in the same way.

$$69 - 45 = 69 - 40 - 5 = 29 - 5 = 24$$

c. 68 − 29 = _____   86 − 48 = _____   74 − 36 = _____   93 − 57 = _____

3. Use any of the *thinking stages* shown above to work out the answers to these problems.

forty-three + eighty-seven = _____   83 take away fifty-eight = _____

Choose some of the sums you have done on this page and show the thinking stages you have used.

ADDITION AND SUBTRACTION

BRIDGING AND ADJUSTING

1. The two sums below show the *thinking stages* for getting the correct answer.

$$27 + 8 = 27 + 3 + 5 = 35$$
$$46 + 39 = 46 + 30 + 4 + 5 = 76 + 4 + 5 = 80 + 5 = 85$$

Now do these sums. Try to *think* in the same way as the first example above: 27 + 8.

a. 27 + 6 = _____ 77 + 8 = _____ 6 + 58 = _____ 89 + 9 = _____ 9 + 38 = __

Write out these two calculations in the same way as the second example: 46 + 39.

34 + 68 = _____

57 + 26 = _____

2. Now look at the *thinking stages* in these two problems.

$$33 + 56 = 33 + 60 - 4 = 93 - 4 = 89$$
$$89 - 54 = 89 - 50 - 4 = 39 - 4 = 35$$

a. Add 38 to each number in the box. Use the first example above to help you: 33 + 56.

35		57		34		46		53		48		39	

b. Subtract 27 from each number in the box. Use the second example above to help you: 89 − 54.

58		76		96		69		78		67		87	

3. Complete these problems. Try to use the strategies shown on this sheet.

58 + 8 = _____   58 + 24 = _____   96 − 39 = _____   88 − 45 = _____

Draw two boxes like the ones in part 2 and write in the same starting numbers. Add and subtract different two-digit amounts from each number.

+ AND – WHOLE NUMBERS, FRACTIONS, DECIMALS

1. Fill in the charts. Think carefully about the easiest way to find the answers.

+	9	41	49	51	19	31	59	11	39	21	29
23			72								
47									86		
35					54						

–	11	41	29	25	19	9	21	15	49	31	39
87							66				
74											35
56	15										

2. Work out the answers to these problems. Think carefully. Don't panic!

a. $\dfrac{2}{2} + \dfrac{6}{3} =$ _____

b. $\dfrac{9}{3} - \dfrac{12}{6} =$ _____

c. $\dfrac{10}{2} - \dfrac{5}{5} =$ _____

d. $\dfrac{8}{4} - \dfrac{4}{4} =$ _____

e. $0.95 - 0.44 =$ _____

f. $0.36 + 0.23 =$ _____

3. Work out these problems.

a. Total up £3.25 and £1.06 and subtract your answer from £5. _____

b. 6.23 metres minus 123 centimetres equals _____ centimetres.

c. How much greater than £1.25 is two pounds ninety-nine? _____

d. What is the difference in pence between 655p and £2.50? _____

e. $\dfrac{1}{5}$ of 15 metres is how many centimetres? _____

Draw either an addition or subtraction chart. Write in your own set of two-digit numbers across the top and down the side and then fill it in.

QUICK MENTAL MATHS

PLACE VALUE WHEN ADDING AND SUBTRACTING

1. Write the answers to these problems in words.

a. 4006 + 6 = _____

b. 4100 – 40 = _____

c. 4650 – 50 = _____

d. 4 + 6000 = _____

e. 6200 – 160 = _____

2. Write down what the value of the 1 stands for in the answers to these calculations.

a. 14cm + 7cm _____   **c.** 996kg + 26kg _____   **e.** 22.3m + 0.8m _____

b. 211g – 21g _____   **d.** 36ml – 17ml _____   **f.** £9.90 – £0.89 _____

3a. Do each problem. Write the answers in the first column. In the second column, arrange the answers according to size with the smallest number at the top.

5674 – 9	5665	
5647 + 8		
5572 – 7		
5650 + 6		

b. Do each problem. Write the answers in the first column. In the second column, arrange the answers according to size with the largest number at the top.

8 + 781	789	
7.99 – 0.10		
78.1 + 0.8		
910 – 13		

c. Break down this number into ThHTU.

six thousand, three hundred and ninety-one = 6000 + _____ + _____ + _____

Use the digits 2, 3, 4 and 7 and see how many ThHTU numbers of different values you can write down. Do the same with 1, 5, 6 and 8.

QUICK MENTAL MATHS

ADDING AND SUBTRACTING SEVERAL NUMBERS

1. Add together each column of numbers and write your answer in the box. Use strategies such as looking for pairs that make 10, 20, and putting the largest number first.

9	3	10	5	8	12	1
5	4	8	2	15	6	8
13	7	11	4	3	6	6
9	17	7	8	10	12	8
7	9	9	16	5	4	14

2. Solve these addition and subtraction problems.

a. From one hundred and twenty-six subtract 10 and 6. _____

b. What number is left when 4, 6 and 11 are taken away from 90? _____

c. 213 plus 421 plus 133 equals _____

3. Complete these subtraction chains.

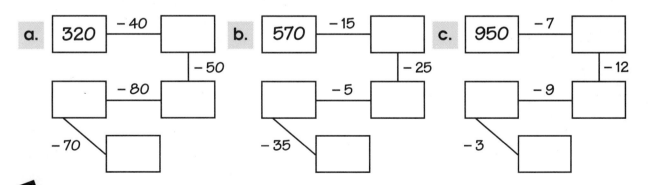

a. 320 — 40 [ ] — 50 [ ] — 80 [ ] — 70 [ ]

b. 570 — 15 [ ] — 25 [ ] — 5 [ ] — 35 [ ]

c. 950 — 7 [ ] — 12 [ ] — 9 [ ] — 3 [ ]

Invent some more subtraction chains like the ones above but make them longer. Try some addition chains or a mixture of both addition and subtraction. Good luck!

NAME   CLASS

TEST YOUR SKILLS 1 (B1–B6)

B1 Write the missing numbers to these addition facts.

a. 34 + 36 = 70   d. 48 + 42 = ☐   g. 48 + 32 = ☐

b. 15 + 25 = ☐   e. 24 + 46 = ☐   h. 51 + 29 = ☐

c. 33 + 17 = ☐   f. 28 + 32 = ☐   i. 33 + 57 = ☐

B2 Fill in this subtraction chart.

−	43	30	47	32	25	40	36	27	38	50	45
13			34								
18										32	

B3 Complete this set of sums by filling in the empty spaces.

123 + 9 = _____ | 9 + _____ = 132 | _____ − 123 = 9 | 132 − _____ = 123

B4 Work out the answers to these calculations

a. 22 − 11 = 11   c. 32 − 16 = ☐   e. 59 + 41 = ☐

b. 13 + 87 = ☐   d. 25 + 75 = ☐   f. 34 − 17 = ☐

B5 Make four addition sums from these numbers. Use each number only once. Put the largest number first. Now work out all your sums.

____ + ____ = ____ | 175 | 145 | 37 | 91 | ____ + ____ = ____

____ + ____ = ____ | 54 | 73 | 135 | 155 | ____ + ____ = ____

B6 Find the answer to these near doubles.

78 + 80 = _____   90 − 44 = _____   230 + 233 = _____

TOTAL

TEST YOUR SKILLS 2 (B7–B12)

B7 Fill in the two addition squares and the subtraction grid.

14	21	
	13	21
22		

23		34
	5	
42	16	

–	142	242
13		
23		219

B8 Fill in the missing numbers in the *thinking stages* of these sums.

a. $47 + 66 = 47 + 3 + 66 -$ _____ $=$ _____ $+ 63 = 113$

b. $78 - 36 = 78 - 30 -$ _____ $= 48 - 6 =$ _____

c. $53 + 28 =$ _____ $+ 20 + 3 + 8 = 70 +$ _____ $= 81$

B9 Now fill in the missing amounts in the *thinking stages* of these sums.

a. $43p + 46p =$ _____ $p + 50p - 4p = 93p - 4p =$ _____ p

b. $£69 - £44 = £69 - £$ _____ $- £4 = £29 - £4 = £$ _____

B10 Work out these fraction, decimal and whole number calculations.

a. $\dfrac{12}{4} + \dfrac{8}{2} =$ ____ c. $£4.75 - £3.34 =$ ____ e. $48p + 110p =$ ____

b. $\dfrac{10}{5} - \dfrac{5}{5} =$ ____ d. $0.45m + 0.15m =$ ____ f. $47g - 29g =$ ____

B11 Write down the value of the 7 in the answers to these problems.

$21 - 14 =$		$99 - 23 =$		$350 + 350 =$	
$49 + 23 =$		$32 - 15 =$		$750 - 38 =$	

B12 Solve this problem.

Subtract 8m and 4m from 100m and add $\dfrac{1}{2}$ km to the answer.

TOTAL

MULTIPLICATION FACTS

1. Write in the missing amounts.

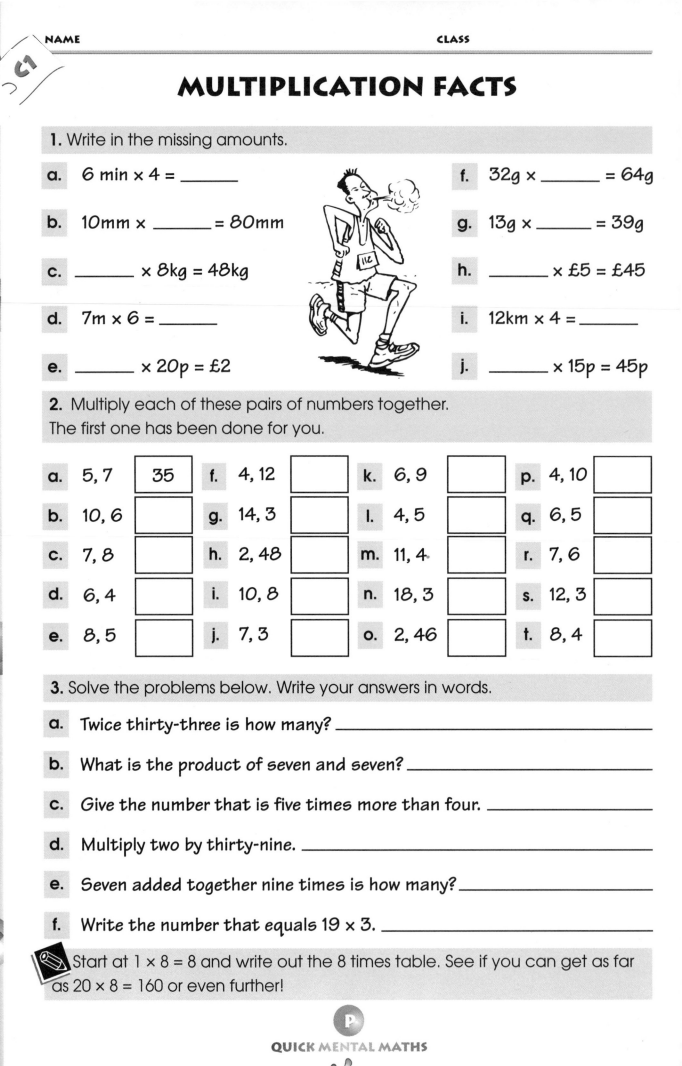

a. 6 min x 4 = _____

b. 10mm x _____ = 80mm

c. _____ x 8kg = 48kg

d. 7m x 6 = _____

e. _____ x 20p = £2

f. 32g x _____ = 64g

g. 13g x _____ = 39g

h. _____ x £5 = £45

i. 12km x 4 = _____

j. _____ x 15p = 45p

2. Multiply each of these pairs of numbers together.
The first one has been done for you.

a. 5, 7	35	**f.** 4, 12		**k.** 6, 9		**p.** 4, 10	
b. 10, 6		**g.** 14, 3		**l.** 4, 5		**q.** 6, 5	
c. 7, 8		**h.** 2, 48		**m.** 11, 4		**r.** 7, 6	
d. 6, 4		**i.** 10, 8		**n.** 18, 3		**s.** 12, 3	
e. 8, 5		**j.** 7, 3		**o.** 2, 46		**t.** 8, 4	

3. Solve the problems below. Write your answers in words.

a. Twice thirty-three is how many? _____

b. What is the product of seven and seven? _____

c. Give the number that is five times more than four. _____

d. Multiply two by thirty-nine. _____

e. Seven added together nine times is how many? _____

f. Write the number that equals 19 x 3. _____

Start at 1 x 8 = 8 and write out the 8 times table. See if you can get as far as 20 x 8 = 160 or even further!

DIVISION FACTS

1. In the three columns below connect each division to the correct answer.

a.			**b.**			**c.**		
	$12 \div 3$	8		$40 \div 8$	9		$39 \div 3$	42
	$76 \div 2$	19		$27 \div 3$	5		$72 \div 8$	9
	$32 \div 4$	4		$36 \div 4$	16		$84 \div 2$	13
	$56 \div 8$	7		$30 \div 6$	27		$54 \div 6$	6
	$95 \div 5$	7		$80 \div 5$	9		$24 \div 4$	9
	$42 \div 6$	38		$54 \div 2$	5		$65 \div 5$	13

2. Work out the answers to these number problems.
Give your answers in words.

a.   How many sets of three in forty-two? _____

b.   Work out a half of seventy-eight. _____

c.   How many times can four be taken from twenty? _____

d.   What number is a sixth of thirty-six? _____

3. Complete these division charts. Some squares have been filled in for you.

÷	20	36	60	48	24	68	32	44	28	64	40	56	52
2				24									
4										16			

÷	60	78	54	90	36	24	42	96	66	30	72	48	84
3		26											
6								16					

Start at $9 \div 9 = 1$, $18 \div 9 = 2$...and see how far you can get. Can you reach
$180 \div 9 = 20$?

RELATIONSHIP BETWEEN × AND ÷

MULTIPLICATION AND DIVISION

1. Fill in the missing bits to complete these sets.
The first one has been done for you.

a. 4 × 7 = 28, 7 × 4 = 28, 28 ÷ 7 = 4, 28 ÷ 4 = 7

b. 2 × 49 = _____   49 × 2 = _____   98 ÷ 49 = 2 _____

c. 17 × 3 = _____   3 × 17 = 51 _____   51 ÷ 17 = _____

d. 4 × 15 = 60 _____   60 ÷ 15 = _____   60 ÷ 4 = _____

e. _____   8 × 6 = _____   48 ÷ 8 = _____   48 ÷ 6 = _____

2. The four sentences below all have the amounts 16cm, 5cm and 80cm in them. In the same way write out four sentences using the amounts 16cm, 3cm and 48cm.

16cm multiplied by 5 equals 80cm _____

5cm times by 16 equals 80cm   _____

80cm divided by 5 equals 16cm   _____

80cm shared by 16 equals 5cm   _____

3a. In the right-hand box, write a division fact using all three numbers from the left-hand box.

4, 10, 40	40 ÷ 10 = 4
7, 3, 21	
56, 8, 7	
8, 6, 48	
5, 75, 15	

b. In the right-hand box, write a multiplication fact using all three numbers from the left-hand box.

13, 39, 3	3 × 13 = 39
4, 36, 9	
35, 7, 5	
72, 2, 36	
9, 54, 6	

Now make up some more sets of four facts using three figures and the ×, ÷ and = signs. Use numbers from the 7, 8 and 9 times tables.

DOUBLES, HALVES, QUARTERS AND EIGHTHS

1. Double these amounts. The example below shows a method of *thinking* that may help you.

$$\text{double } 38 = 30 + 30 + 8 + 8 = 60 + 16 = 76$$

a. 16cm ☐   e. 49p ☐   i. 18kg ☐   m. 48p ☐

b. 38ml ☐   f. 27g ☐   j. 36m ☐   n. 26cm ☐

c. 29km ☐   g. 46m ☐   k. 28g ☐   o. 19km ☐

d. 47kg ☐   h. £37 ☐   l. £39 ☐   p. 17ml ☐

2. Write down in figures half of each of these odd numbers.

a. seven _____   c. three _____   e. thirteen _____

b. fifteen _____   d. seventeen _____   f. nine _____

3. Find a quarter of these numbers by first finding a half and then halving your answer. Like this:

$$60 \div 2 = 30, 30 \div 2 = 15, \text{ so } 15 = \frac{1}{4} \text{ of } 60$$

a. $56 \div 2 \div 2 =$ ☐   c. $72 \div 2 \div 2 =$ ☐   e. $96 \div 2 \div 2 =$ ☐

b. $84 \div 2 \div 2 =$ ☐   d. $64 \div 2 \div 2 =$ ☐   f. $68 \div 2 \div 2 =$ ☐

Find an eighth of these numbers by halving, halving and halving again. Like this:

$$120 \div 2 = 60, 60 \div 2 = 30, 30 \div 2 = 15 \text{ so } 15 = \frac{1}{8} \text{ of } 120$$

g. $80 \div 2 \div 2 \div 2 =$ ☐   h. $104 \div 2 \div 2 \div 2 =$ ☐

i. $112 \div 2 \div 2 \div 2 =$ ☐

Do some more calculations to find quarters and eighths like the ones above. You will need numbers that are multiples of four to get quarters and multiples of eight to get eighths.

PARTITIONING WHEN MULTIPLYING

1. This example shows a way of *thinking* that may help you work out the problems on this sheet.

$$24 \times 2 = (20 \times 2) + (4 \times 2) = 40 + 8 = 48$$

Write out your *thinking stages* as you do these problems. Use the example to help you.

a. 43 × 2 _____

b. 3 × 23 _____

c. 32 × 4 _____

d. 2 × 44 _____

e. 27 × 2 _____

2. Try and *think* in the same way as you work out the answers to the following calculations.

a. 56 × 2 ☐   **d.** 5 × 23 ☐   **g.** 34 × 5 ☐   **j.** 2 × 74 ☐

b. 4 × 41 ☐   **e.** 26 × 8 ☐   **h.** 8 × 14 ☐   **k.** 47 × 3 ☐

c. 18 × 6 ☐   **f.** 3 × 32 ☐   **i.** 35 × 4 ☐   **l.** 4 × 48 ☐

3. Read these questions and work out the correct answers.

a. If a box has a mass of 18kg what is the total mass of five boxes? _____

b. A newspaper costs 35p. What would the price of 6 papers be? _____

c. Oranges are packed 34 to a tray, 4 trays to a box. How many oranges are there in a box? _____

Write out your thinking stages for the multiplications that you did in part 2. Look at the example at the top of the page to help you.

QUICK MENTAL MATHS

DIVISION WITH REMAINDERS

1. Fill in these charts. Write down the divisions first and then the remainders underneath.

÷	57	83	91	62	89	73
4			22			
r			3			
5					17	
r					4	

÷	75	65	95	87	101	109
6		10				
r		5				
7				12		
r				3		

2. Read these questions carefully before answering them.

a. If a straw measuring 20cm is cut into six 3cm lengths what length of

the straw is left over? _____

b. How many remain when 137 is divided by ten? _____

c. A farmer has 114 sheep in his field. He takes them out in groups of 4.

How many groups does he have? _____ How many sheep remain? _____

3. Write in the answers and how many there are remaining.

a. 77 min ÷ 3 = [   ] r [   ]   **f.** £102 ÷ 8 = [   ] r [   ]

b. 93mm ÷ 5 = [   ] r [   ]   **g.** 98km ÷ 6 = [   ] r [   ]

c. 112kg ÷ 6 = [   ] r [   ]   **h.** 111p ÷ 5 = [   ] r [   ]

d. 82m ÷ 4 = [   ] r [   ]   **i.** 70ml ÷ 4 = [   ] r [   ]

e. 105g ÷ 2 = [   ] r [   ]   **j.** 88cm ÷ 3 = [   ] r [   ]

Divide some odd numbers by 4 and 6 and show your remainders as a fraction, for example, $43 \div 4 = 10 \text{ r } 3$ or $10\frac{3}{4}$; $47 \div 6 = 7 \text{ r } 5$ or $7\frac{5}{6}$.

MULTIPLICATION AND DIVISION

CALCULATION PATTERNS (× AND ÷)

1. Fill in the numbers in these multiplication patterns and then complete the sentences.

a.	20	22								36	
b.		44			56	60					
c.				39	42		48				
d.									102	108	114
e.		55	60							90	
f.	100						150	160			

g. To find the answers to the ×5 table multiply by _____ and then halve.

h. The answers to the ×3 table facts are half those of the _____ facts.

i. To multiply by _____ multiply by 10 and then double.

j. The answers to the _____ table facts are half those of the ×10 facts.

k. To find the _____ table facts double the ×4 facts.

2. These questions are about the multiplication chart at the top of the page.

a. Which row of numbers is the answers to the a) ×6 table? _____

b) ×4 table? _____

b. Which times tables always have
a) even answers? _____

b) odd and even answers? _____

3. Fill in the numbers in the empty squares to make this pattern complete.

14	×		=	
÷		÷		÷
2	×		=	8
=		=		=
	×		=	7

Make up some of your own times and share patterns like those in part 3.

C8

FACTORS AND MULTIPLYING BY 10, 100, 1000

1. Write out all four factors for the following numbers.

a. 6 _____

c. 14 _____

e. 22 _____

b. 8 _____

d. 15 _____

f. 26 _____

Write down as many factors as you can think of for these amounts.

g. 5 _____

i. 9 _____

k. 16 _____

h. 18_____

j. 24 _____

2. Make these amounts 10, 100 and 1000 times larger.

	×10	×100	×1000
a. £10		£1000	
b. 6.5m			6500m
c. 1.35g	13.5g		
d. 7p		700p	
e. 3.8km			3800km

	×10	×100	×1000
f. 0.25g		25g	
g. 2.02g			
h. 4.9km			
i. 4p			
j. 3.16g			

3. Join each number in a starburst to a number 100 times larger in a box. One has been done for you.

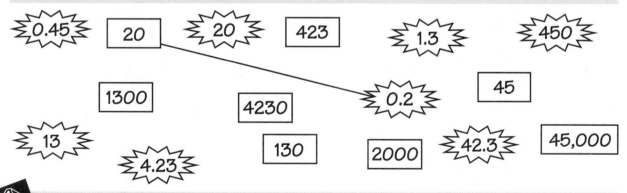

Make a list of the numbers between 1 and 30 that only have two factors. What is the special name for this type of number?

DIVIDING BY 10, 100, 1000

1. Make these amounts 10, 100 and 1000 times smaller.

		÷ 10	÷ 100	÷ 1000
a.	2780m	278m		
b.	6700km			6.7km
c.	£43,000		£430	
d.	4060g	406g		
e.	9000p		90p	

		÷ 10	÷ 100	÷ 1000
f.	2430g			2.43g
g.	3000p			
h.	680g			
i.	7500m			
j.	£6000			

2. Join each number in a box to a number 100 times smaller in a starburst. One has been done for you.

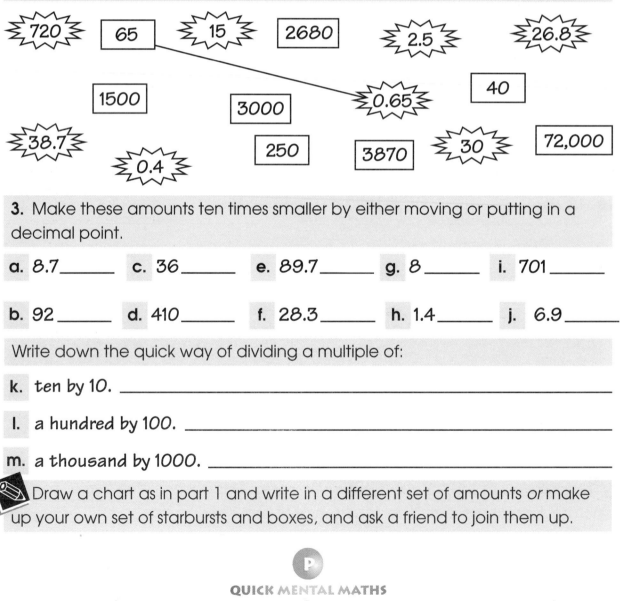

3. Make these amounts ten times smaller by either moving or putting in a decimal point.

a. 8.7_____   c. 36_____   e. 89.7_____   g. 8_____   i. 701_____

b. 92_____   d. 410_____   f. 28.3_____   h. 1.4_____   j. 6.9_____

Write down the quick way of dividing a multiple of:

k. ten by 10. _____

l. a hundred by 100. _____

m. a thousand by 1000. _____

Draw a chart as in part 1 and write in a different set of amounts *or* make up your own set of starbursts and boxes, and ask a friend to join them up.

USING RELATED × AND ÷ FACTS

1. Look at the example below and then write out the other problems in the same way.

$$8 \times 7 = 56, 7 \times 8 = 56, 56 \div 8 = 7, 56 \div 7 = 8$$

a. 13×3 _____

b. 4×12 _____

c. 8×7 _____

d. 6×9 _____

e. 4×8 _____

2. Work out these sets of problems. The answers can already be seen if you look closely!

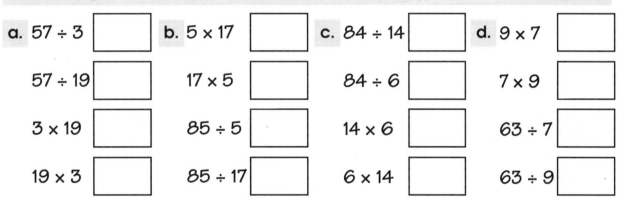

a. $57 \div 3$ ☐   **b.** 5×17 ☐   **c.** $84 \div 14$ ☐   **d.** 9×7 ☐

$57 \div 19$ ☐ 17×5 ☐ $84 \div 6$ ☐ 7×9 ☐

3×19 ☐ $85 \div 5$ ☐ 14×6 ☐ $63 \div 7$ ☐

19×3 ☐ $85 \div 17$ ☐ 6×14 ☐ $63 \div 9$ ☐

3. This example shows you a method of *thinking* that will help you with the calculations below.

$$\tfrac{1}{2} \text{ of } 143 = \tfrac{1}{2} \text{ of } 140 \text{ plus } \tfrac{1}{2} \text{ of } 3 = 70 \text{ plus } 1\tfrac{1}{2} = 71\tfrac{1}{2}$$

Answer these questions. Show your *thinking stages* in the same way as the example.

a. $\tfrac{1}{2}$ of 225m = _____

b. $\tfrac{1}{2}$ of 263g = _____

The sums in part 3 are called close halves. Make up some similar calculations. Your starting numbers do not have to end in an odd digit.

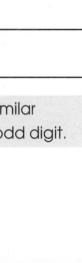

PLACE VALUE WHEN MULTIPLYING AND DIVIDING

1. Write the answers to these problems in words.

a. 5342 × 2 = _____

b. 8664 ÷ 2 = _____

c. 3012 × 3 = _____

d. 6903 ÷ 3 = _____

e. 2001 × 4 = _____

2. Write down the value of the five in the answers to these calculations.

a. 250cm ÷ 5 _____   **c.** 2kg × 250 _____   **e.** 630m ÷ 6 _____

b. 3.5g × 3 _____   **d.** 4.08ml ÷ 8 _____   **f.** £9.00 × 5 _____

3a. Do each problem. Write the answer in the first column. In the second column, arrange the answers according to size with the smallest number at the top.

b. Do each problem. Write the answer in the first column. In the second column, arrange the answers according to size with the largest number at the top.

8 × 40	320	
459 ÷ 3		
45 × 3		
416 ÷ 2		

6.93 ÷ 3	2.31	
71 × 3		
63.9 ÷ 3		
710 × 3		

c. Break down the answer to this multiplication problem into ThHTU.

three thousand, one hundred and five × 3 = 9000 + _____ + _____ + _____

Draw some abacuses to show your answers to part 1. Underneath each abacus write in figures the amount that it shows.

QUICK MENTAL MATHS

× AND ÷ WHOLE NUMBERS, FRACTIONS, DECIMALS

1a. Divide these numbers by 6 and multiply the answer by 5.

60	36	18	48	96	42	24	54	78	66	30	84	72	90
		3					9						
	30									25			

b. Divide these numbers by 8 and multiply the answer by 4.

40	16	72	8	56	32	88	24	48	64	80
		9				11				
		36							32	

2. Do the problems below. Be careful!

a. $1.5 \times 5 =$ ☐

c. $1\frac{3}{4} \times 3 =$ ☐

e. $96 \div 4 =$ ☐

b. $800 \div 10 =$ ☐

d. $4.2 \div 6 =$ ☐

f. $\frac{1}{2} \times 5 =$ ☐

3. Solve these calculations. They are all to do with fractions and decimals.

a. Find $\frac{3}{4}$ of 36. _____

f. $0.7 \times 0.4 =$ _____

b. 16 quarters is how many ones? _____

g. $4.8 \div 4 =$ _____

c. Two thirds × 6 equals _____

h. $1\frac{1}{5} \times 5 =$ _____

d. 0.5 × 5 equals how many halves? _____

i. $4\frac{1}{2} \div 2 =$ _____

e. 10 times $\frac{4}{5}$ equals _____

j. $2 \times \frac{5}{8} =$ _____

Multiply these fractions by 3, 5 and 8 and write your answers as both a top-heavy fraction and a decimal fraction. $\frac{1}{2}$, $\frac{3}{4}$, $\frac{2}{5}$

TEST YOUR SKILLS 1 (C1–C6)

MULTIPLICATION AND DIVISION

C1   Multiply each of these pairs of numbers together.

a. 2, 35 ☐   d. 5, 25 ☐   g. 19, 5 ☐

b. 9, 3 ☐   e. 6, 9 ☐   h. 4, 23 ☐

c. 14, 4 ☐   f. 8, 60 ☐   i. 16, 3 ☐

☐

C2   Divide the largest number in these pairs by the smallest.

a. 70, 2 ☐   d. 8, 40 ☐   g. 2, 92 ☐

b. 4, 56 ☐   e. 400, 5 ☐   h. 36, 6 ☐

c. 48, 6 ☐   f. 3, 54 ☐   i. 8, 80 ☐

☐

C3   a. Write a division fact using all three numbers on the left.   **b.** Write a multiplication fact using all three numbers on the left.

7, 28, 4		6, 12, 72	
80, 5, 16		92, 4, 23	

☐

C4   Work out $\frac{1}{2}$, $\frac{1}{4}$ and $\frac{1}{8}$ of each amount in that order.

thirty-two ____ ____ ____   forty-eight ____ ____ ____

fifty-six ____ ____ ____   sixty-four ____ ____ ____

sixteen ____ ____ ____   eighty ____ ____ ____

☐

C5   Do these sums by multiplying the tens first and then the ones.

23 × 5 = ____   6 × 38 = ____   22 × 8 = ____   4 × 43 = ____

☐

C6   Write in the answers and how many there are remaining.

109cm ÷ 8 = ☐ r ☐   £104 ÷ 6 = ☐ r ☐

☐

TOTAL ☐

TEST YOUR SKILLS 2 (C7–C12)

C7 Complete the number pattern in the table below.

	8	9	10	11	12	13	14	15
×6	48				72			
	16				24			

C8 Write down the factors for the following numbers.

12 _____ 20 _____

Make these amounts 10, 100 and 1000 times larger.

	×10	×100	×1000
£0.50			

	×10	×100	×1000
4.07g			

C9 Make these amounts 10, 100 and 1000 times smaller.

	÷10	÷100	÷1000
6060m			

	÷10	÷100	÷1000
320g			

C10 Work out these two sets of sums. All the sums in a set are related.

a. $64 ÷ 4 =$ _____ $16 × 4 =$ _____ $64 ÷ 16 =$ _____ $4 × 16 =$ _____

b. $5 × 14 =$ _____ $70 ÷ 5 =$ _____ $14 × 5 =$ _____ $70 ÷ 14 =$ _____

C11 Write down the value of the 8 in the answers to these questions.

$255kg ÷ 3 =$ _____ $4 × 700km =$ _____ $£0.40 × 20 =$ _____

C12 Do two things to the number in the top row. Divide it by 5. Multiply it by 3.

	15	$\frac{25}{5}$	12.5	40
3	45			

MULTIPLICATION AND DIVISION

C14

ADDING, SUBTRACTING AND MULTIPLYING

1. Write in the missing amounts.

a. $(6g + 42g) - (3g + 8g) =$ _____

f. 3 months x _____ = 2 years

b. 4ml + _____ + 6ml = 25ml

g. ¾ + 2 ¼ + ⁵⁄₂ = _____

c. 9 hours x _____ = 36 hours

h. _____ x 2 x 10 = 1 metre

d. 2cm + 12cm = 23cm − _____

i. _____ = 23 − 5 − 4 − 3 − 6 − 2

e. 1 x 27kg = _____ x 3kg

j. 5 + 12 + 6 + 3 + 14 = _____

2. Work out the answers to these number problems.

a. By how much is 16 minus 9 less than forty-one multiplied by 2? _____

b. By how much is 42 add eight greater than nine add thirty-three? _____

c. Treble sixty, take away 5 x 10, equals how many? _____

d. Twice seventy-five multiplied by six will give what number? _____

e. Find the sum of the odd numbers between 4 and 12. _____

3. Multiply each pair of numbers together, add 50 to the answer and then subtract half from the total.

a. 4, 3	e. 3, 10	i. 7, 6	m. 19, 2
b. 7, 4	f. 9, 4	j. 9, 10	n. 3, 6
c. 6, 6	g. 5, 8	k. 3, 14	o. 4, 15
d. 17, 2	h. 8, 6	l. 4, 11	p. 18, 3

Choose other pairs of numbers like those in part 3 above. Carry out the same steps. What happens if the total is an odd number after you have added 50?

MULTISTEP AND MIXED OPERATIONS

MULTIPLYING, DIVIDING AND ADDING

1. Look at the example that has been done for you. It will help you to solve the other problems.

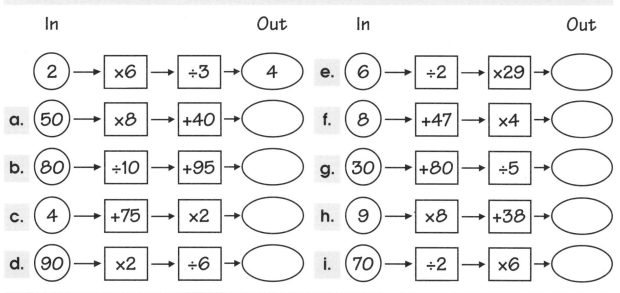

2. Read these problems and then write down the answers.

a. By how much is 38 add 17 greater than 42 divided by six? _____

b. What is the cost of 3 items at 25p each and 5 items at 20p each? _____

c. In a bag of 15 apples three of them are green and the rest are red.

What fraction of the apples are green? _____ red? _____

d. Divide five hundred by 4 and multiply the answer by three. _____

3. Using the ×, ÷, and = signs make up eight problems that all have three different signs in them like this: (16 + 26) ÷ 7 = 6 or 5 × (9 + 6) = 75. Use brackets if you need to.

_____

_____

Make up some of your own In/Out sums like the ones at the top of the page. Remember to use all three signs. Try to make up some longer sums with more instructions in the middle.

ADDING, MULTIPLYING AND SUBTRACTING

1. Work out the answers to these calculations. In your head, do the parts in brackets first. Think like this: $(3 \times 6) + (2 \times 40) = 18 + 80 = 98$.

a. $(6 \times 4) + (4 \times 4) =$ _____

f. $(6 \times 5) - (3 \times 5) =$ _____

b. $(15 + 15) \times (12 + 8) =$ _____

g. $(2 \times 43) - (5 \times 7) =$ _____

c. $(6 \times 6) - (5 \times 5) =$ _____

h. $(50 - 38) \times (101 - 98) =$ _____

d. $(7 \times 10) + (3 \times 15) =$ _____

i. $(4 \times 5) + (6 \times 4) =$ _____

e. $(45 - 39) \times (17 - 12) =$ _____

j. $(50 \times 8) - (4 \times 80) =$ _____

2. Subtract the smallest number from the larger, double the answer and then add 9.

a. 50, 31 ☐   **d.** 46, 18 ☐   **g.** 40, 23 ☐   **j.** 41, 72 ☐

b. 26, 14 ☐   **e.** 12, 42 ☐   **h.** 27, 45 ☐   **k.** 13, 84 ☐

c. 17, 38 ☐   **f.** 37, 24 ☐   **i.** 19, 44 ☐   **l.** 98, 15 ☐

Add the two numbers together, multiply the answer by 4 and then subtract 5.

m. 5, 5 ☐   **p.** 18, 12 ☐   **s.** 32, 58 ☐   **v.** 3, 9 ☐

n. 5, 8 ☐   **q.** 34, 36 ☐   **t.** 24, 26 ☐   **w.** 9, 11 ☐

o. 4, 7 ☐   **r.** 23, 17 ☐   **u.** 47, 33 ☐   **x.** 35, 25 ☐

3. Solve these number problems.

a. From three times three times seven subtract thirteen. _____

b. Make 4 twice the size, multiply the answer by 6, then add 75. _____

Using the +, ×, – and = signs, make up twelve more sums with brackets like those in part 1.

SUBTRACTING, DIVIDING AND ADDING

1. Take away 15p from each amount, divide the answer by six and then add 12p.

63p	87p	33p	75p	51p	105p	93p	111p	39p	81p	99p	45p	69p	57p
				36p									
				6p									
				18p									

2. Look at the example that has been done for you. It will help you solve the others.

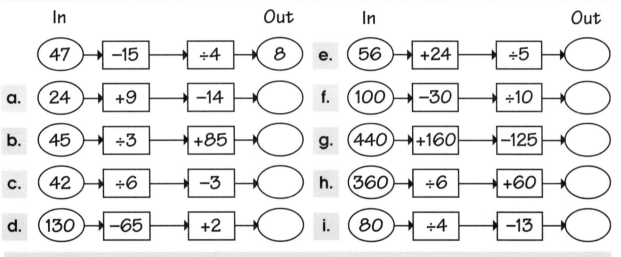

In → Out

47 → −15 → ÷4 → 8

a. 24 → +9 → −14 → ◯

b. 45 → ÷3 → +85 → ◯

c. 42 → ÷6 → −3 → ◯

d. 130 → −65 → +2 → ◯

In → Out

e. 56 → +24 → ÷5 → ◯

f. 100 → −30 → ÷10 → ◯

g. 440 → +160 → −125 → ◯

h. 360 → ÷6 → +60 → ◯

i. 80 → ÷4 → −13 → ◯

3. Read these questions and work out the answers.

a. Take nine and seven away from forty and share the answer by 3.

b. What number is sixteen more than five add four?

c. Divide ninety-four by 2 and subtract the answer from 25 + 25.

d. Subtract sixteen from eighty and halve the answer.

e. Double sixteen, plus 15, minus nine equals how many?

 Make up a money chart like the one in part 1. Make sure that you write clear instructions about what you have to do with each amount.

A1

1. a. **£3.25**, **£3.31**, £3.37, £3.43, **£3.49**, £3.55, £3.61
   b. 500m, **475m**, **450m**, 425m, 400m, **375m**, 350m

2. a. **100**, 95, 90, 85, 80, 75, 70, 65, 60, 55, **50**.
   b. Yes c. − 7 − 6 − 5 − **4** − 3 − 2 − **1 0 1 2 3 4 5 6 7 8 9**

3. a.

20	22	24	**26**	28	30	32	34	36	**38**	40
40	44	**48**	52	56	60	**64**	68	72	76	80
30	33	36	39	**42**	45	48	51	54	57	**60**
60	**66**	72	78	84	90	96	102	**108**	114	120

   b. The ×4 answers are double ×2.
   The ×6 answers are double ×3.

A2

1. a. 29 b. 306 c. 630 d. 2004 e. 320
   f. 8060 g. 9470 h. 5652 i. 7910

2. a. seventy-two b. six hundred and eight
   c. eight hundred and twenty d. thirty-five
   e. four thousand, two hundred and fifty
   f. two thousand, four hundred and five

3. a. 4 b. 8765 c. 2000 d. 20 e. 500 f. 3000

A3

1. a. > b. < c. > d. < e. > f. > g. < h. >
   i. < j. > k. < l. >

2. a. no b. yes c. yes d. no e. no f. yes
   g. 3725kg h. 8002g i. open-ended – accept any number greater than 6999

3. a. 9876, 8967, 7898, 7896, 6987, 6978, 6789
   b. £8.60, £6.80, £6.50, £6.08, £5.80, £5.60, £5.10, £1.50

A4

1. a. 20, 18cm b. 650, 680ml c. 80, 75hrs
   d. 30, 28km e. 200, £212 f. 500, 496m
   g. 2000, 2100mm h. 12, £13 i. 400, 397m
   j. 3000, 3240g

2. 100, 250, 400, 550, 700, 850

3. a. Open-ended – numbers should be roughly: 75, 41, 610, 1500, 2000
   b. Open-ended – numbers should be roughly: 100, 75, 1500, 600, 750

A5

1. a. 110km, 290km, 660km, 4010km
   b. £9.00, £10.00, £10.00, £1.00
   c. 7m, 4m, 10m, 27m

2.

210 miles	200 miles	b. 4500
120 miles	100 miles	Accept any number
200 miles	200 miles	between 151 and
160 miles	200 miles	199.
50 miles	100 miles	
410 miles	400 miles	

3. a. 4 hours b. 10 litres c. 6 metres d. 122km
   e. 26cm f. £2.00 g. 2 hours h. 8 litres

A6

A1. a. **£2.28**, £2.21, £2.14, **£2.07**, £2.00, £1.93
   b. **345g**, **395g**, 445g, 495g, 545g, **595g**
   c. 6025, **5725**, **5425**, 5125, **4825**, 4525
   d. **95**, 91, 87, 83, 79, 75, 71, 67, 63, 59, **55**
   e. Yes

A2. a. 6552, 9988, 6300 b. 2049 c. 700 d. 5408

A3. a. 8506, 7943, 7934, 7439, 7394, 3140, 3104, 3041
   b. 0.1 $\frac{1}{5}$ 0.3 $\frac{2}{5}$ $\frac{1}{2}$ 0.6 0.7 $\frac{4}{5}$ $\frac{9}{10}$ 1

A7

A4. a. 1000, 2500, 3250, 4500, 5500, 7000
   b. Following sums or numbers should be shaded: 300 + 600, 700 − 100, 700, 20

A5. a.

6520km	6500km	7000km
4370km	4400km	4000km
4260km	4300km	4000km
6670km	6700km	7000km

   b. 2 hours c. 5 litres d. 3 metres e. 17cm
   f. £4.00 g. 3 hours

B1

1. **a.** 50 min **b.** 22mm **c.** 15kg **d.** 100m
e. 1 litre **f.** 380g **g.** £53.00 **h.** 600km
i. 19p **j.** 26 hours

2. **a.** 60 **b.** 70 **c.** 90 **d.** 80 **e.** 80 **f.** 90 **g.** 70 **h.** 80
i. 60 **j.** 70 **k.** 60 **l.** 90 **m.** 80 **n.** 70 **o.** 80

3. **a.** ninety **b.** fifty **c.** seventy **d.** ninety
e. forty-five

B5

1. **a.** 151 + 37 + 4 = 192
b. 235 + 12 + 9 = 256
c. 320 + 55 + 8 = 383
d. 465 + 24 + 11 = 500
e. 756 + 16 + 14 = 786

2. **a.** 79p **b.** 62 **c.** 99p

3. Open-ended – ten addition sums using all the numbers given. (Check that the largest number has been written first and that a TU number has been paired with a HTU number.)

B2

1.
a. 5	b. 15	c. 5
25	35	30
15	40	30
10	5	20
25	5	10
10	20	45

2. **a.** twenty-eight **b.** six
c. one hundred and seventy-five **d.** forty-two

3.
24	**17**	14	26	22	37	16	27	23	12	25	13	15
33	26	23	35	31	**46**	25	36	32	21	34	22	24
13	6	3	15	11	26	5	16	**12**	1	14	2	4
35	28	25	37	33	48	27	38	34	23	36	24	**26**
16	9	6	**18**	14	29	8	19	15	4	17	5	7

B6

1. **a.** 122 **b.** 103 **c.** 61 **d.** 164 **e.** 143 **f.** 82
g. 261 **h.** 285 **i.** 237 **j.** 179 **k.** 218 **l.** 298

2. **a.** £50 + £50 – £3 – £2 = £95
b. 90p + 90p – 2p – 4p = 174p
c. 70m + 70m + 10m or 80m + 80m – 10m = 150m
d. 70g + 70g – 10g or 60g + 60g + 10g = 130g

3. **a.** 94 **b.** 290 **c.** 114

B3

1. **a.** (completed example) **b.** 81, 54,
27 + 54 = 81 **c.** 77, 77 – 29 = 48, 29
d. 93 – 57 = 36, 57, 93 **e.** 89 – 15 = 74, 15, 89, 89

2. (in any order) – £38.00 add £43.00 equals £81.00; £43.00 plus £38.00 equals £81.00; £81.00 minus £38.00 equals £43.00; £81.00 subtract £43.00 equals £38.00

3. These addition facts with numbers in any order: **(23 + 28 = 51)** (35 + 36 = 71) (45 + 27 = 72) (56 + 34 = 90) (25 + 46 = 71) Subtraction facts using the three numbers given: (63, 39, 24) (83, 57, 26) (91, 63, 28) (81, 44, 37) (63, 35, 28)

B7

1. **a.** 7, 11, 17, 57, 117, 517
b. **418**, 118, 48, 18, 11, 8
c. **6**, 8, 16, 36, 116, 316
d. **622**, 122, 72, 22, 17, 12

2.
11	**14**	**25**		**16**	**8**	24		**20**	50	**70**
9	12	**21**		17	**15**	**32**		25	**35**	60
20	**26**	46		**33**	23	56		**45**	**85**	130

3.
15	16	17	**18**		65		144	145	146	147
14	15	**16**	17		55		133	134	135	136
13	**14**	15	16		45		122	123	124	125
12	13	14	15		35		111	112	113	114

B4

1. **a.** 10 **b.** 14 **c.** 18 **d.** 12 **e.** 20 **f.** 16 **g.** 26
h. 22 **i.** 24 **j.** 30 **k.** 32 **l.** 28 **m.** 34 **n.** 38
o. 36 **p.** 40

2. **a.** 47cm **b.** 58ml **c.** 81 hrs **d.** 15p **e.** 33km **f.** £6
g. 53cm **h.** 84g **i.** 79 litres **j.** 62m **k.** 30kg
l. 42 min

3. **a.** 25, 32, 38, 45, 24, 30
b. 32, 38, 35, 49, 40, 27
c. 41, 94, 40, 29, 42, 9

B8

1. **a.** 27 + 68 = 27 + 3 + 68 – 3 = 30 + 65 = 95
b. 438 + 9 = 438 + 2 + 7 = 440 + 7 = 447
c. 953, 776, 532, 706

2. **a.** 52 + 26 = 50 + 20 + 2 + 6 = 70 + 8 = 78
b. 78, 97, 149, 151
c. 39, 38, 38, 36

3. 130, 25

B9

1. a. 33, 85, 64, 98, 47
b. 34 + 68 = 34 + 60 + 6 + 2 = 94 + 6 + 2 = 100 + 2 = 102
c. 57 + 26 = 57 + 20 + 3 + 3 = 77 + 3 + 3 = 80 + 3 = 83

2. a.

35	73	**57**	95	**34**	72	**46**	84	**53**	91	**48**	86	**39**	77

b.

58	31	**76**	49	**96**	69	**69**	42	**78**	51	**67**	40	**87**	60

3. 66, 82, 57, 43

B10

1.

32	64	**72**	74	42	54	82	34	62	44	52
56	88	96	98	66	78	106	58	**86**	68	76
44	76	84	86	**54**	66	94	46	74	56	64

76	46	58	62	68	78	**66**	72	38	56	48
63	33	45	49	55	65	53	59	25	43	**35**
45	**15**	27	31	37	47	35	41	7	25	17

2. a. 3 b. 1 c. 4 d. 1 e. 0.51 f. 0.59

3. a. 69p b. 500cm c. £1.74 d. 405p e. 300cm

B11

1. a. four thousand and twelve
b. four thousand and sixty
c. four thousand six hundred
d. six thousand and four
e. six thousand and forty

2. a. 1cm b. 100g c. 1000kg d. 10ml
e. 0.1m (10cm or $\frac{1}{10}$) f. £0.01 (1p or £ $\frac{1}{100}$)

3.

5665	5565		**789**	897
5655	5655		7.89	789
5565	5656		78.9	78.9
5656	5665		897	7.89

c. 6000 + 300 + 90 + 1

B12

1. 43, 40, 45, 35, 41, 40, 37

2. a. 110 b. 69 c. 767

3. a. **320**, 280, 230, 150, 80
b. **570**, 555, 530, 525, 490
c. **950**, 943, 931, 922, 919

B13

B1. a. 70 b. 40 c. 50 d. 90 e. 70 f. 60
g. 80 h. 80 i. 90

B2.

30	17	**34**	19	12	27	23	14	25	37	32
25	12	29	14	7	22	18	9	20	**32**	27

B3. 132, 123, 132, 9

B4. a. 11 b. 100 c. 16 d. 100 e. 100 f. 17

B5. Open-ended – four addition sums using all the numbers given. (Check that the largest number has been written first.)

B6. 158, 46, 463

B14

B7.

14	**21**	35		**23**	11	**34**		129	229
8	**13**	**21**		19	**5**	24		119	**219**
22	34	56		**42**	**16**	58			

B8. a. 3, 50 b. 6, 42 c. 50, 11

B9. a. 43p, 89p b. £40, £25

B10. a. 7 b. 1 c. £1.41 d. 0.60m e. 158p f. 18g

B11.

7		70		700
70		7		700

B12. 588m

C1

1. a. 24 min b. 8 c. 6 d. 42m e. 10 f. 2
g. 3 h. 9 i. 48km j. 3

2. a. 35 b. 60 c. 56 d. 24 e. 40 f. 48 g. 42
h. 96 i. 80 j. 21 k. 54 l. 20 m. 44 n. 54 o. 92
p. 40 q. 30 r. 42 s. 36 t. 32

3. a. sixty-six b. forty-nine c. twenty
d. seventy-eight e. sixty-three f. fifty-seven

C2

1.

a. 4	b. 5	c. 13
38	9	9
8	9	42
7	5	9
19	16	6
7	27	13

2. a. fourteen b. thirty-nine c. five d. six

3.

10	18	30	**24**	12	34	16	22	14	32	20	28	26
5	9	15	12	6	17	8	11	7	**16**	10	14	13

20	**26**	18	30	12	8	14	32	22	10	24	16	28
10	13	9	15	6	4	7	**16**	11	5	12	8	14

C3

1. a. (completed example)
b. 98, 98, 98 ÷ 2 = 49
c. 51, 51 ÷ 3 = 17, 3 d. 15 × 4 = 60, 4, 15
e. 6 × 8 = 48, 48, 6, 8
2. (in any order) – 16cm multiplied by 3 equals 48cm; 3cm times by 16 equals 48cm; 48cm divided by 3 equals 16cm; 48cm shared by 16 equals 3cm.
3. a. These division facts with numbers in any order: **(40 ÷ 10 = 4)** (21 ÷ 7 = 3) (56 ÷ 8 = 7) (48 ÷ 6 = 8) (75 ÷ 5 = 15)
b. Multiplication facts using the three numbers given: (13, 3, 39) (4, 9, 36) (7, 5, 35) (2, 36, 72) (9, 6, 54)

C4

1. a. 32cm b. 76ml c. 58km d. 94kg e. 98p f. 54g g. 92m h. £74 i. 36kg j. 72m k. 56g l. £78 m. 96p n. 52cm o. 38km p. 34ml
2. a. $3\frac{1}{2}$ b. $7\frac{1}{2}$ c. $1\frac{1}{2}$ d. $8\frac{1}{2}$ e. $6\frac{1}{2}$ f. $4\frac{1}{2}$
3. a. 14 b. 21 c. 18 d. 16 e. 24 f. 17 g. 10 h. 13 i. 14

C5

1. a. 43 × 2 = (40 × 2) + (3 × 2) = 80 + 6 = 86
b. 3 × 23 = (3 × 3) + (20 × 3) = 9 + 60 = 69
c. 32 × 4 = (30 × 4) + (2 × 4) = 120 + 8 = 128
d. 2 × 44 = (2 × 4) + (40 × 2) = 8 + 80 = 88
e. 27 × 2 = (20 × 2) + (7 × 2) = 40 + 14 = 54
2. a. 112 b. 164 c. 108 d. 115 e. 208 f. 96 g. 170 h. 112 i. 140 j. 148 k. 141 l. 192
3. a. 90kg b. 210p (£2.10) c. 136 oranges

C6

1.

14	20	**22**	15	22	18
1	3	**3**	2	1	1
11	16	18	12	**17**	14
2	3	1	2	**4**	3

12	**10**	15	14	16	18
3	**5**	5	3	5	1
10	9	13	**12**	14	15
5	2	4	**3**	3	4

2. a. 2cm b. 7 c. 28 r 2
3. a. 25min r 2min b. 18mm r 3mm c. 18kg r 4kg d. 20m r 2m e. 52g r 1g f. £12 r £6 g. 16km r 2km h. 22p r 1p i. 17ml r 2ml j. 29cm r 1cm

C7

1. a. **20**, **22**, 24, 26, 28, 30, 32, 34, **36**, 38
b. 40, **44**, 48, 52, **56**, **60**, 64, 68, 72, 76
c. 30, 33, 36, **39**, **42**, 45, **48**, 51, 54, 57
d. 60, 66, 72, 78, 84, 90, 96, **102**, **108**, **114**
e. 50, **55**, **60**, 65, 70, 75, 80, 85, **90**, 95
f. 100, 110, 120, 130, 140, 150, 160, 170, 180, 190 g. ×10 h. ×6 i. 20 j. ×5 k. ×8
2. a. (a) row d (b) row b
b. (a) ×2, ×4, ×6, ×10 (b) ×3, ×5
3.

14	×	4	=	56
÷		÷		÷
2	×	4	=	8
=		=		=
7	×	1	=	7

C8

1. a. 6: 1, 6, 2, 3 b. 8: 1, 8, 2, 4
c. 14: 1, 14, 2, 7 d. 15: 1, 15, 3, 5
e. 22: 1, 22, 2, 11 f. 26: 1, 26, 2, 13
g. 5: 1, 5 h. 18: 1, 18, 2, 3, 6, 9 i. 9: 1, 9, 3
j. 24: 1, 24, 2, 3, 4, 6, 8, 12 k. 16: 1, 16, 2, 4, 8
2. a. £100, **£1000**, £10,000 b. 65m, 650m, **6500m** c. **13.5g**, 135g, 1350g d. 70p, **700p**, 7000p e. 38km, 380km, **3800km** f. 2.5g, **25g**, 250g g. 20.2g, 202g, 2020g h. 49km, 490km, 4900km i. 40p, 400p, 4000p j. 31.6g, 316g, 3160g
3. **(0.2–20)** (0.45–45) (13–1300) (450–45000) (20–2000) (1.3–130) (42.3–4230) (4.23–423)

C9

1. a. **278m**, 27.8m, 2.78m
b. 670km, 67km, **6.7km**
c. £4300, **£430**, £43 d. 406g, 40.6g, 4.06g e. 900p, **90p**, 9p f. 243g, 24.3g, **2.43g** g. 300p, 30p, 3p h. 68g, 6.8g, 0.68g i. 750m, 75m, 7.5m j. £600, £60, £6
2. **(65–0.65)** (1500–15) (3000–30) (250–2.5) (2680–26.8) (3870–38.7) (40–0.4) (72,000–720)
3. a. 0.87 b. 9.2 c. 3.6 d. 41 e. 8.97 f. 2.83 g. 0.8 h. 0.14 i. 70.1 j. 0.69
k. remove a nought l. remove two noughts
m. remove three noughts

C10

1. a. 13 × 3 = 39, 3 × 13 = 39, 39 ÷ 13 = 3, 39 ÷ 3 = 13
b. 4 × 12 = 48, 12 × 4 = 48, 48 ÷ 4 = 12, 48 ÷ 12 = 4 c. 8 × 7 = 56, 7 × 8 = 56, 56 ÷ 8 = 7, 56 ÷ 7 = 8 d. 6 × 9 = 54, 9 × 6 = 54, 54 ÷ 6 = 9, 54 ÷ 9 = 6 e. 4 × 8 = 32, 8 × 4 = 32, 32 ÷ 4 = 8, 32 ÷ 8 = 4
2.

a.	b.	c.	d.
19	85	6	63
3	85	14	63
57	17	84	9
57	5	84	7

3. a. $\frac{1}{2}$ of 220 plus $\frac{1}{2}$ of 5 = 110 plus $2\frac{1}{2}$ = $112\frac{1}{2}$ m b. $\frac{1}{2}$ of 260 plus $\frac{1}{2}$ of 3 = 130 plus $1\frac{1}{2}$ = $131\frac{1}{2}$ g

C11

1. a. ten thousand, six hundred and eighty-four **b.** four thousand, three hundred and thirty-two **c.** nine thousand and thirty-six **d.** two thousand, three hundred and one **e.** eight thousand and four

2. a. 50cm **b.** $\frac{5}{10}$g or 0.5g **c.** 500kg **d.** $\frac{5}{10}$ ml or 0.5ml **e.** 5m **f.** £5.00

3.

320	135	2.31	2130
153	153	213	213
135	208	21.3	21.3
208	320	2130	2.31

c. 9000 + 300 + 10 + 5

C12

1.

10	6	**3**	8	16	7	4	**9**	13	11	5	14	12	15
50	**30**	15	40	80	35	20	45	65	55	**25**	70	60	75

5	2	**9**	1	7	4	**11**	3	6	8	10
20	8	**36**	4	28	16	44	12	24	**32**	40

2. a. 7.5 **b.** 80 **c.** $5\frac{1}{4}$ **d.** 0.7 **e.** 24 **f.** $2\frac{1}{2}$

3. a. 27 **b.** 4 **c.** 4 **d.** 5 **e.** 8 **f.** 0.28 **g.** 1.2 **h.** 6 **i.** $2\frac{1}{4}$ **j.** $1\frac{1}{4}$

C13

C1. a. 70 **b.** 27 **c.** 56 **d.** 125 **e.** 54 **f.** 480 **g.** 95 **h.** 92 **i.** 48

C2. a. 35 **b.** 14 **c.** 8 **d.** 5 **e.** 80 **f.** 18 **g.** 46 **h.** 6 **i.** 10

C3. a. These division facts with numbers in any order: (28 ÷ 7 = 4) (80 ÷ 5 = 16)
b. Multiplication facts using the three numbers given: (6, 12, 72) (92, 4, 23)

C4. 32: 16, 8, 4 **56:** 28, 14 7 **16:** 8, 4, 2 **48:** 24, 12, 6 **64:** 32, 16, 8 **80:** 40, 20, 10

C5. 115, 228, 176, 172
C6. 13cm r 5cm, £17 r £2

C14

C7.

48	54	60	66	**72**	78	84	90
16	18	20	22	**24**	26	28	30

C8. 12: 1, 12, 2, 3, 4, 6   **20:** 1, 20, 2, 4, 5, 10
£5.00, £50.00, £500.00   40.7g, 407g, 4070g

C9. 606m, 60.6m, 6.06m   32g, 3.2g, 0.32g
C10. 16, 64, 4, 64
70, 14, 70, 5
C11. 80kg, 800km, £8.00

C12.

15	$\frac{25}{5}$	12.5	40	
3	45	1	15	2.5	37.5	8	120

D1

1. a. 37g **b.** 15ml **c.** 4 **d.** 9cm **e.** 9 **f.** 8 **g.** $5\frac{1}{2}$ **h.** 5cm **i.** 3 **j.** 40

2. a. 75 **b.** 8 **c.** 130 **d.** 900 **e.** 32

3. a. 31 **b.** 39 **c.** 43 **d.** 42 **e.** 40 **f.** 43 **g.** 45 **h.** 49 **i.** 46 **j.** 70 **k.** 46 **l.** 47 **m.** 44 **n.** 34 **o.** 55 **p.** 52

D2

1. a. 440 **b.** 103 **c.** 158 **d.** 30 **e.** 87 **f.** 220 **g.** 22 **h.** 110 **i.** 210

2. a. 48 **b.** £1.75 **c.** one fifth ($\frac{1}{5}$) four fifths ($\frac{4}{5}$) **d.** 375

3. Open ended – eight sums all with three different signs in them chosen from ×, ÷, + and =.

D3

1. a. 40 **b.** 600 **c.** 11 **d.** 115 **e.** 30 **f.** 15 **g.** 51 **h.** 36 **i.** 44 **j.** 80

2. a. 47 **b.** 33 **c.** 51 **d.** 65 **e.** 69 **f.** 35 **g.** 43 **h.** 45 **i.** 59 **j.** 71 **k.** 151 **l.** 175 **m.** 35 **n.** 47 **o.** 39 **p.** 115 **q.** 275 **r.** 155 **s.** 355 **t.** 195 **u.** 315 **v.** 43 **w.** 75 **x.** 235

3. a. 50 **b.** 123

D4

1.

48p	72p	18p	60p	36p	90p	78p	96p	24p	66p	84p	30p	54p	42p
8p	12p	3p	10p	6p	15p	13p	16p	4p	11p	14p	5p	9p	7p
20p	24p	15p	22p	18p	27p	25p	28p	16p	23p	26p	17p	21p	19p

2.

8	16
19	7
100	475
4	120
91	7

3. a. 8 **b.** 25 **c.** 3 **d.** 32 **e.** 38